A Story (
Shra

A Story of Duty
Shravan

AMRITA SHARMA

LEARNERS PRESS PRIVATE LIMITED

Published by
LEARNERS PRESS PRIVATE LIMITED
L-11 Green Park Extension, New Delhi-110016

Cover design by Neelu Vishwa
Illustrations by Jaswinder

Printed at Prolific Incorporated, New Delhi-110020.

Contents

Introduction

This is the tale of Shravan, an ordinary person, born into a humble and poor family, who, through sincere performance of his duty towards his parents, has become immortal, and worthy of great respect.

Shravan is a perfect example of a dutiful son. He believed that in duty lies devotion and godliness. He was far from the conventional system of worship to God and prayers. The whole purpose and meaning of his life revolved around his parents; and serving them with his meagre resources. He is the ideal son, who lived and died for his parents.

Shravan did not possess wealth but was full of devotion and reverence towards his parents. He was not only their eyes, but also a willing support for their aged and weak bodies. Most of all, he was the dutiful son who considered it his responsibility, to serve his parents to the best of his abilities.

It was this selfless devotion, this abounding love and respect, and deep-rooted sense of duty towards his parents, that enabled him to fulfil all their wishes. To him, his parents were his Gods, his temples, and his very objects of worship. In their service lay his greatest happiness and source of serenity—that itself was his pilgrimage. He held his parents in high esteem and considered it an honour to die in their service.

So awe-inspiring was his devotion that all sages and Gods began considering him to be worthy of their respect. His single-minded pursuit of duty made Shravan a symbol of duty, for all ages.

1

Childhood

Long ago, there was a small village on the banks of a river. It was a serene place where people of different castes lived in harmony.

In the same village, there lived a blind couple with their one and only son, Shravan Kumar. The family belonged to the Vaishya caste. The Vaishyas are the lower caste, below the Brahmins and the Kshatriyas but above the Shudras or the untouchables.

The old couple often fell short of money, and many a times had to go without food. But the blind couple loved their son very much, and always thanked God for blessing them so. They gave the son all the love and blessings they could.

"Shravan, we are so unfortunate that we cannot give you anything, but our blessings," his father would say.

"You have to face so many difficulties because you were born to us!" said his father.

Shravan touching their feet, replied, "No, dear parents, please don't say that. I'm so fortunate that I was born to you both. You have given me so much love. Of what use would wealth and comforts be, if there was no love!" And together, they would bear all their misfortunes with great courage and strength.

Even as a little child, Shravan would help his parents as much as he could. He would take his father out for walks, along the river. There, Shravan's father would take his bath. While his father bathed, Shravan collected fruits and berries from the trees, and the juicy roots from some plants which he gave his father to eat. After his father's bath, they would walk back home together.

"Shravan, may God bless you! These berries are really juicy," said his father, enjoying the luscious fruits.

"Have more of these, Father. I have enough here with me to take home, even for Mother," said Shravan.

Shravan would even help his mother with the household chores. While other children would be playing together outside, Shravan would be busy sweeping the house, washing the dishes, or collecting dry wood and sticks for his mother to cook in the evening. Early in the morning, he would pick up the pitcher and leave for the river, to get fresh drinking water. Then he would go out again to pick fresh flowers of all colours and sizes, so that his mother

could make a garland out of it and place it on her Lord's idol. His mother would immediately know that he was back, with the flowers, as its fragrance would fill the room each time he entered.

"How lovely they smell, Shravan. Where did you find such fragrant flowers!" his mother would ask and pat his head.

"Oh, I just had to look around a little!" replied Shravan. He never told her that he swam across the river and back, to get her the most fragrant flowers.

He never felt tired of serving his parents. Many a times, his mother would come up to him in the evenings, and say, "Shravan, why don't you go out and play with your friends for sometime? There is nothing to be done at the moment!" But Shravan always shook his head and sat down by her side.

"No Mother, I don't feel like going anywhere. Here, give me the vegetables. I will cut them for you," he said, and would sit down to cut the vegetables.

At night, he always served the food to his parents, and after they were through with dinner, he would tuck them to bed. He even pressed their feet till they were fast asleep. Only then, did he go to sleep himself. Shravan's life revolved around his parents and their well-being.

2

A Devoted Youth

As Shravan grew up, his parents became more dependent on him. He cooked meals, picked fruits and vegetables, and even washed clothes. Every morning, he took the clothes to the riverside and spent hours washing and drying them. And in the evenings, after his parents had finished their prayers, he would sit by their feet and listen to their words of wisdom.

The old couple used to really enjoy telling him stories of yore, and other mythological tales.

"Today, I shall tell you the story of Raja Harishchandra. He was a good king, loved and adored by all his subjects. He was even respected by the Gods because he was a righteous man and a just king. To him, justice and honesty were the only religion. It was these qualities which caused him a lot of suffering, but nothing could deter him from the righteous path. Even Gods respected him for that...," his father would go on and on, while his

mother counted her rosary. And Shravan would sit and listen rapturously about all the brave and virtuous kings and princes, and he learnt a lot from these tales.

Shravan also took up the job of cutting woods and trees, which was enough for their modest meals. His parents spent their time praying and meditating. But in the evenings they would wait eagerly for their son's

return. He was the centre of their lives. The moment he would enter the house, their faces would light up and all their worries would vanish. He always brought them joy and they blessed him with their hearts.

As time passed, Shravan's parents began to feel older. They felt that the time was nearing for them to renounce their bodies. They began to feel closer to God with every passing day. They wished in their hearts that if only they could visit the holy places of God before they died, they would indeed be blessed.

"But how is that possible? We are both blind and old, and we have no money either. How can we possibly go," sighed the old ascetic.

"You are right, it's not possible," said his wife. "God will understand our problems. He knows how much we wish to go on the pilgrimage, but there is no way we can do it."

And the two let their wish lie deep in their hearts. But Shravan, knew them very well. He realised their unhappiness. He could make out their unspoken wish by their long sighs as they sat listening to the temple bells, and as they sat in prayers longer than before. They would try and be cheerful whenever Shravan was around, but he knew that something was amiss.

One day, he went up to his parents and said, "Father, what is it? Why are you and Mother, so sad? Have I failed you in any way, have I hurt your feelings in some way?" Both his parents were surprised at this.

"Oh no, Son, it's nothing like that. You are mistaken. We are as happy as anyone can be with a son like you," said his father, fondly reaching out his hand to touch Shravan's head.

But Shravan fell at his parents' feet, and said, "Then why do you look so unhappy. I would be the most unfortunate person on the earth if I can't make my parents happy. My life is worthless if I can't serve those who gave me birth and brought me up in spite of many hardships, who love me immensely and to whom I am indebted for my very life! I would be nothing less then an animal or a beast who forgets his parents just as soon as he is old enough to be on his own. If I have failed as a son, in any way, please tell me because I am not aware of it. But don't be unhappy or angry towards me for not being able to serve you as best as I should."

At this his father caught him by the shoulders and lifted him up, while his mother held his face lovingly in her hands and wiped his tears away. "Son, how can we be angry or displeased with you, ever! You have been the very blessing of God, a boon that was granted to us for our good deeds in the past. Even though he took away our sight, he gave us you in return. You are the apple of our eyes. It's because of you that we are alive. In you, we found our purpose to live and love. We are so grateful to God for giving you as our son," said the mother.

But Shravan was not convinced. Folding his hands, he turned to his parents, "Then what is it that makes you unhappy?" he persisted.

At this, his father sighed and said, "It has nothing to do with you Son! We are both growing old now, and soon our end will come. At this last phase of our life, we wished to visit all the holy places to express our gratitude to God for granting us a son like you. But we are old and blind. There's no way we can go to these far-off places, and that is what makes us unhappy."

"But don't worry Son. So what if we can't go on a pilgrimage. We shall pray here, sincerely and with all our heart, and God will understand," said his mother, and blessed him.

3

Finding a Way

That night Shravan could not sleep at all. His parents' sad faces kept haunting him. He lay thinking of how he could fulfil his parents' wishes. He pondered over the possibility of walking, but immediately shrugged it off.

'All these places are so far-off that my parents would surely not be able to take the stress. Oh, if only I could go on their behalf, and offer their prayers for them,' he thought, but then shook his head. He knew it would not be the same. His parents wanted to go themselves, and he had to find a way for it.

He lay awake the whole night trying to figure out a way. For him his parents' happiness was the most important. He cried at his failure and helplessness to find a way. He had no means to take them—no bullock cart, or even a donkey. He felt very sad and began praying to God sincerely.

"Oh God, what do I do? You know how much my parents want to go on this pilgrimage, and how much I want to make it possible. You hear everybody's prayers. Please hear mine too. You are the only one who can do something about it. Please show me the way to fulfil my parents' wishes," he prayed. Then, just as the new day was dawning, he saw a milkman with a bamboo stick on his shoulder, and two big and heavy milk cans on either side, balancing each other. This suddenly gave him the idea.

'Yes! I can take my parents, like this. All three of us can be together, and I shall carry them on my own shoulders.

God has shown me the way, and he will take care of the other things too,' he thought and sat up excitedly. The first thing he did was to look for a thick bamboo stick.

His parents were asleep, when he headed for the forest with two big pitchers. He collected many bamboo sticks of different sizes, and filling the pitchers with water so as to try the weight, he hung them on either side. But many of the sticks broke when he hung the heavy pitchers, and he wondered if he would actually be able to carry out his idea. Then he found a bamboo stick that was thicker than all the ones he had tried before.

'Yes, this looks just fine. I think it will take the weight of the pitchers on

it,' he thought, and hung the pitchers on either side. And to his joy, he found that the stick held on just fine.

"Oh, thank you God. I think I can finally take my parents on their pilgrimage. I can't wait to tell them about my plan," he said, excitedly, and ran home with his bamboo stick and the pitchers.

At home, his parents had woken up and were wondering where he had gone without informing them. When he saw them, Shravan ran faster and on reaching them, he touched their feet.

"Where were you Shravan? We were worried," said his mother.

"Mother, I had something very important to do. Father, you also come here. I have to talk to you both," he said and made his father sit before him with his mother. Then he said, "Both of you wanted to go on a pilgrimage, and I am going to take you there."

His parents were surprised. "But Shravan, how can you take two old and blind people without anything to travel in," asked his father.

"Oh, I have thought about it, Father. All I need is your consent and blessing," replied Shravan. He explained to his father, how they were all to go. When his parents heard this, they were thrilled. They hugged Shravan and cried tears of joy.

"Oh Shravan, may God bless you. You have made us so happy today. We are indeed blessed to have you. You have been such a good son to us. Just undertaking this pilgrimage will bring us the peace of mind we need. You don't know how much this means to us Shravan. We shall feel most content with life, as long as we get to visit all the holy places by ourselves. Oh Shravan, may God always be with you!" they said.

That day, Shravan asked his parents to get their things ready. Meanwhile, he went out to the forest, to collect as many fruits as he could. He chose the best of them, and went home. "We shall leave early in the morning tomorrow," he told his parents, who were too excited to sleep that night.

The next morning, just as the birds began chirping, Shravan set off with his parents on the pilgrimage. He made them sit on either side, and carefully balancing the bamboo stick on his firm shoulders, he took God's name, and started on their long journey.

4

The Journey Begins

It was a cool morning, and the sun was not shining too brightly. At first they went very slowly, but as they moved on, Shravan began walking a little faster.

"Shravan, are you all right? We must be very heavy for you," asked his mother.

"It's a long journey ahead. How far can you take us like this," said his father.

"Don't worry, Father, I can manage, and when I am tired. I shall immediately stop," replied Shravan, and they proceeded further.

On the way, everyone who saw them were amazed at the way this devoted young boy was carrying his parents. They shook their heads in disbelief and respect, and some smiled in admiration. But Shravan did not notice anything at all. His mind was fixed only on getting his parents to the holy places.

By noon, they stopped under the shade of a banyan tree and Shravan told his parents to rest.

"Both of you must be tired from sitting, you should take some rest. Meanwhile, I will also refresh myself," he said. His parents willingly got down and washed their hands and feet with water, while Shravan dusted the place clean and laid down the sheets for them to lie on. And while Shravan went to the riverside and washed himself, they rested under the cool shade. Feeling fresh and strong again, Shravan

collected more fruits and went back to his parents. He gave them the fruits to eat and cool water to drink.

"Now we will stop only in the evening, so it's better to eat well," said Shravan.

"Don't worry Shravan. The fruits are so fresh and juicy, that we have already eaten more than enough," said his father and handed some fruits to Shravan too. After they had all finished eating, they set off again.

This time, Shravan did not stop at the next village, and by the time it was evening, he was exhausted. "Shravan, you have been walking the whole day. Let's stop now. There's no hurry really," said his mother, and Shravan agreed.

"Yes Mother, we will stop at the very next village that comes. I'm tired too," he said. And so, they stopped again, just after the sun had set in the distant horizon. Shravan found a nice big tree, and after sweeping the place clean with a thick, dry branch, he spread the sheets for his parents to lie on. Then he went to sleep himself. Early next morning, he pulled out some water from a nearby well, and his parents washed themselves. Then after a short meal of fruits and milk, that Shravan got from a milkman, the three resumed their journey. They passed various places on the way, and met many people who were so amazed at the sight of this young boy carrying his parents that they would come up to them and talk.

"So you are going on a pilgrimage. You must go to Kashi also. There are beautiful temples, and one feels close to God there," some people would say... or "You are really lucky to have the chance of going on a pilgrimage. I would also love to go, but at the moment, I can't," ... or some others would even say, "Please pray on our behalf too. God will not refuse your prayers..." There were many

like them whom Shravan and his parents met whenever they stopped to rest.

They walked for days on end, stopping here and there before they finally reached Kashi, which was a very important and well-known place of pilgrimage.

It is a beautiful city, situated on the banks of the holy river Ganga. It was believed that *rishi* Bhagirath, had induced Lord Indra to send Goddess

Ganga from heaven to earth to redeem mankind. At Lord Indra's orders, Ganga descended on earth, but at such great speed that everyone panicked.

The rishi knew that she would destroy everything if she did not slow down. He then prayed to Lord Shiva, who lived in the Kailash mountains of the great Himalayas, to do something about it. Hearing the prayers, Lord Shiva caught Ganga in the coil of his hair, and from there he released her gently, whereby she descended on the earth and flowed throughout the country, purifying all that came in the way.

The Hindus believe that Ganga is pure and has become more purified and sacred from her stay in Lord Shiva's hair. Anyone who takes a dip in her holy water becomes pure and is cleansed of all one's past sins. When Shravan along with his parents entered the holy city, they were thrilled at the sound of the temple bells ringing and the hymns that were being chanted.

"Shravan, I can't wait to take a dip in the holy waters," said his excited father. And Shravan gently led his father to the river, and helped him wash himself in it. Then he took his mother and helped her take a dip in the Ganga too.

As they dried themselves, Shravan brought some flowers which they wanted to place at the God's feet. Then he took them to the temple and helped

them to offer their prayers and flowers to God. As they came out, Shravan made them sit on the corner of the stairs, so that they could hear the holy *mantras* being sung by the priests.

"Shravan, may God bless you for the joy you have brought us," said his parents, and he bowed his head at their feet.

That night they slept inside the temple premises. Early next morning, they set off again for the next pilgrimage site. It was a long journey and sometimes it got very hot. Shravan would often stop to refill their small pitcher with water, and he devotedly wiped the dust off his parents feet and arms, whenever they passed a dusty road on the way. After many days of stopping here and there, they reached another holy city.

There too, Shravan's parents prayed and spent the whole day inside the temple. They ate the *prasad* that was being offered by the priest.

"If not for Shravan, we would never have tasted this food of God. I can't believe we are actually on a pilgrimage. I had never thought it could be possible," the father would often tell Shravan's mother. And they smiled and wept at the same time. His father called

Shravan to them and touching his head fondly, he said, "Shravan, you have given a lot of happiness to your old and blind parents. We really feel indebted to you for what you have done for us."

At this, Shravan fell at his parents' feet and clasping them, he said, "Oh Father, don't ever say that again. I would be cursed if I were to ever hold you in my debt. I have done nothing unusual. I have only tried to fulfil my duty as a son."

Shravan and his parents almost covered all the holy places. They visited Rishikesh, where the weather was pleasant. He religiously took his parents to the temples, helped them to climb the stairs and offer their prayers. For Shravan, the joyous and contented look on his parents' face as they visited each of these holy places was reward enough.

From there, they went to Haridwar, where he helped them to bathe in the holy waters of Ganga again. He made sure that they had ample rest before they resumed their journey. For days they travelled, stopping over at villages or just in some nearby fields or under a tree, only to leave at daybreak. They even managed to go to Dwarka which had once been the kingdom of Lord Krishna. At the end of his incarnation as an *avatar* of Lord Vishnu, the ancient kingdom of Dwarka had been deluged by the sea. However, the believers still

feel the Lord's presence in the temples dedicated to him.

Shravan's parents were delighted to be in this holy city. His father said, "You know Shravan, this particular place gives me a lot of peace. It's a place where the Lord resided. Here, I feel near to God and can thus die peacefully."

Then they sat through the evening prayers, and ate the food that was being served to all the pilgrims, in the temple itself. They rested there for the night, and after the early morning prayers, they set off again.

5

King Dashratha and Shravan

After a few more places of pilgrimage, they reached Ayodhya which was ruled by the Kosala king, Dashratha. After offering their respects at the temples there, Shravan and his parents decided to spend the night in the city itself as they were too tired to travel. Shravan soon found a small hut on the outskirts of the city, in the forest, and it was not too far from the river Sarayu either.

"We shall stay in this hut for the night. There is no one here," said Shravan to his parents.

"Are you sure we are not intruding in someone's house son," asked his father, as Shravan held his hand and led him inside.

"No, Father, probably an ascetic used to live here, but it looks like the place has been vacant for quite sometime now," replied Shravan. "In any case, it's just for the night. We'll be gone tomorrow morning."

"Whatever you say son. We are both very tired too," sighed his father. And so Shravan cleared the place a little so that his parents could lie down comfortably. Then he made his bed outside the hut, and they slept.

A few hours later, Shravan woke up, and heard his mother calling him.

"Yes Mother, what is it?" he asked, entering inside.

"Son, your Father and I are very thirsty. Can we have some water?" asked his mother.

"Yes, of course. I will get it for you in a minute," said Shravan, and went to look for the small pitcher. But when he picked it up, he found that it was empty. He went back to the hut and told his mother that he was going to get some water from the river.

"No, please don't go. It's very dark outside, and there is a forest nearby. In any case we are not very thirsty.

Another few hours, and it will be morning. We can wait," she said.

But Shravan would not hear of it. "Mother, don't worry. The river is close by. I'll be back very soon. Just wait for me," said Shravan, and picking up the pitcher, he left the hut.

Now it so happened that, King Dashratha of Ayodhya, was also in the forest. He had come for hunting without his men. King Dashratha was a very good hunter and a skilled marksman. He could shoot anything just by hearing the sound. He did not even have to see to aim. That night, he was hiding behind the trees and thick bushes, to hunt a big animal.

It was a very quiet night. No breeze blew, and no leaf rustled. As Shravan moved towards the river, he observed the stillness too. But his thoughts were more on getting the water for his thirsty parents. Unaware of any danger lurking in the forest, Shravan bent down to fill the pitcher. But the minute the pitcher touched the still waters, King Dashratha heard the sound, and immediately sat up. 'That sounds like an elephant,' he thought. And listening to the gurgling sound that came from the water filling into the pitcher, it seemed to him like an elephant's trunk.

'This is going to be a big catch,' thought King Dashratha, and picking up his bow and arrow, he concentrated hard. Then, when he was sure of the direction of the sound, he released his arrow. Shravan was about to pick up the pitcher when the arrow tore through his chest, and he shrieked in pain. Falling to the ground, he realised that he had been shot with an arrow, and he tried to pull it out, but in vain.

Meanwhile, King Dashratha had heard the shriek too, and he panicked. "Oh my God! That sounds like a human voice," he said, and rushed in the direction of the sound. On reaching there, he was shocked to see a young boy lying on the ground and moaning. He was writhing with pain, and his whole body was smeared in blood and dust. And when the king saw the broken pitcher lying near him in bits and pieces, he understood the whole thing.

"Oh my God," gasped Dashratha, and ran up to him. Seeing Dashratha, Shravan realised that he was responsible for the shot, and he pleaded with him to pull the arrow out of his chest.

"Please take the arrow out. I'm in great pain!" he moaned. When Dashratha pulled it out, more blood gushed out of his body.

"Oh God, what have I done! How could I, the king of Ayodhya, the protector of my people, the vanquisher of enemies, kill someone so young and innocent! How could I kill someone who had done me no harm at all! Oh God, how could I do this?" cried Dashratha, as he stared at the wounded body.

Hearing this, Shravan tried to console the king in his breathless voice.

"It wasn't your fault King Dashratha. You did not mean to shoot me Any how what is done, cannot be undone. But before I die, I must ask you a favour. My old and blind parents are waiting for me in that hut, in the forest. They are very thirsty. Please take some water for them quickly, and also tell them of my death," he said.

"Yes, of course. I'll take this water for them," said Dashratha, and with that assurance, Shravan breathed his last. Laying him gently, Dashratha with a heavy heart set off to look for Shravan's parents.

Meanwhile, almost an hour had passed since Shravan had been away, and his parents were now getting worried.

"He should have been back by now. I wonder what's taking him so long," said his father anxiously. "I hope he is all right. There's a big forest out there. I told him not to go. I could have done without water till morning. Oh, I just hope he comes back now," said his mother, getting really worried. Just then they heard a noise outside the hut.

"I think he is back ... Shravan, Shravan. Are you back? What took you so long we were worried," said his father. But suddenly stopped when he did not hear anyone speak.

"Shravan, it is you, isn't it? Why don't you say something?" asked his father. At this, Dashratha came forward, and replied, "It's not your son. I'm Dashratha, the king of Ayodhya, and I'm afraid, I have some bad news for you." Hearing this, the old couple panicked.

"What is it? I hope Shravan is all right. Tell me, he is all right," said his father getting up with a start.

"Where is our son? Why isn't he here yet," cried his mother.

Hanging his head in shame, Dashratha replied, "He is dead." He

then related the whole incident to them, and he felt upset when he saw their shock. They stood up in disbelief, and said, "No, this can't be true. Take us to Shravan, wherever he is. He can't be dead. He can't leave his poor blind parents alone. Take us to him," they ordered Dashratha, and the guilty king led them to their son's lifeless body.

When they reached there, the old couple immediately sat down beside Shravan's body. When they found it still and cold, they shrieked with agony.

"This can't be true! Our son can't leave without us! How could you do this to us God... He was young and we were old. If you had to take anyone, it should have been us... Why God, why?" they cried.

And then they turned angrily towards Dashratha and in their wrath, they cursed him. "You have killed our son. You have taken away from us the light of our life, the apple of our eyes, and the very purpose of our existence. You are responsible for causing us this pain, this agony of losing a young son, a son who did so much for his old and

blind parents. You shall not live in peace. You, who have caused us so much suffering, shall suffer the same fate. You too shall bear the anguish of separation from your dearest son, and you shall die in his grief, just as you have caused us to die," they said. Saying this, the old couple hugged their son's body, and holding his head in their lap, they too breathed their last.

Dashratha stood there, stunned at all that had happened. He did not pay much attention to the old couple's curse, but his heart bled nevertheless, from the immense pain he had caused three innocent people. Putting his bow and arrow aside, he collected dry woods and sticks to make their funeral pyres. Lighting them devotedly, he prayed for

their place in heaven and peace of soul, and then he went back to his kingdom. That whole night, he lay awake thinking about the devoted son and how much his parents loved him that they died in the grief of their loss. Little did he know that years later, he was to suffer the same pain, the same anguish of separation from his beloved son, Rama.

6

The Cursed End

Many years had passed since that incident. Meanwhile, King Dashratha became the ruler of Ayodhya. He had three wives, Kaushalya, Sumitra and Kaikeyi, and four sons, namely Rama, Bharat, Lakshmana and Shatrughana. When the sons came of age, King Dashratha decided to crown his eldest son, Rama, as the future king. The whole city was rejoicing, and King Dashratha himself was overwhelmed with joy. He loved his eldest son, Rama, tremendously and he knew that Ayodhya would be in very safe hands with him.

However, fate had willed it otherwise. On the eve of the coronation of Prince Rama, King Dashratha received a big shock from his third wife Kaikeyi. In return for a favour that she had done for him long ago, she demanded that her son, Bharat, be crowned the king, and that Prince Rama be sent to the forest in exile for fourteen long years. When king Dashratha heard of it, he collapsed with grief. He was so badly shaken, that he was bedridden. And when Lord Rama finally, left for the forest, King Dashratha in his anguish, suddenly remembered the curse of the old ascetic, whose son he had unknowingly killed. He confided to his first wife, Kaushalya, the curse of Shravan's parents, and related the whole story to her.

"Kaushalya, today my past has come to punish me. My dearest son is taken away from me. Now I know how the old couple must have felt when they were deprived of their dear son, their very joy in life. I wondered how Shravan's parents could die on being separated from their son, but now I know. I myself see no use of clinging to my life, when my loved one is snatched away from me so cruelly. I too cannot survive the pain," he said, and with his son's name on his lips, he too gave up his life in grief. The curse of the old and blind couple had finally come true.

The Value of Duty

The place of 'Duty' in daily life is very important. Every man, woman and child, has a duty to perform in his or her life. It could be a duty towards one's family, work, nation, fellow human beings, parents and even other living beings.

Duty is something that a person is required to do for moral, ethical, legal or even social reasons, for the well-being of everyone. A person is considered dutiful when one performs the duty that is expected of him. In fact, the duties expected of us, vary according to the situation, circumstances and context that we are placed in. We are required to perform these duties because it is the 'right' thing to do, and because it is essential for a correct and systematic running of things in this world.

We live in a society which is a congregation of various people. Each one has a duty in society, which he/she is not only expected to perform, but which one must fulfil since one is an integral part of the society. For example, it is our duty to keep our country, our city, our locality and our houses clean; to help and protect others around us, to cooperate with the authorities in maintaining law and order, to work towards the progress of our country—all these and many more comprises our social duties.

Similarly, moral duties too are an important ingredient in human lives. To think, see, speak and do good to others, is our primary moral duty. To follow values like honesty, responsibility, faithfulness, devotion, sacrifice, etc., is our moral duty, along with our responsibility to inspire others to do the same.

Ethical duties, are considered very important for the development of a good human being. It is our duty to distinguish and discriminate between what is right and what is wrong. It is also our responsibility to act according to our position and occupation, to be always fair to others and see that justice is carried out at all cost. The strong should always protect the weak, and not harm or abandon them; the young should always help the old and show them the respect that they deserve.

Among these, however, the foremost duty is our parental duty, according to which the children must not only respect, obey and love their parents, but help and protect them in their old age.

According to our Hindu *dharma*, it is only the fulfilment of our duties that increases the value of human lives. Parental duty is the most sacred and invaluable duty of all. The Indians believe that it is the pivotal duty of every person to serve his parents. Every child should take care of his parents when they are old and weak, and are unable to take care of themselves. A parent - child relationship is reversed over the course of time. When a child is small and unable to take care of himself, his parents look after him and his welfare; and when they grow old, it is the child's duty to look after his parents' sustenance and well-being.

The ever flowing love that our parents bestow upon us, the selfless care they shower upon us, the innumerable sacrifices they make for our sake, and the sleepless nights they spend thinking about our welfare is all beyond repayment. One can never be as giving and as selfless as one's parents. However, only if the child performs his duty to them selflessly and with full devotion, can he or she likely find a place in heaven. In the Indian culture, to serve one's parents and to do our duty towards them is regarded as the most pious duty.

The Hindu scriptures and many sages throughout the ages have strongly believed that whoever performs the duties that are required of him, is as worthy of respect and devotion, as any great sage himself.

Almost all the Sikh Gurus believed that one does not have to necessarily be a priest or a man of religion to be a Guru. They all proclaimed that any man who did his duty properly and with full devotion was at the same level as the Guru himself. A farmer who did his duty of tilling the land and growing crops is worthy of respect; a man who teaches his students devotedly is considered worthy; a person who sews clothes with keen interest and concentration is also pious in his own way; and a son who takes care of his parents to the best of his abilities, however, meagre they are, is as saintly and admirable as other men of God.

Gandhiji too believed that whoever performed his duty allotted to him by his position in the family, in the society or in the country was a great man. According to him, any man who gave importance to the duty he had to do, was to be worshipped. And that is why Eklavya, the devoted disciple of Guru Dronacharya, who considered it his duty to give *guru dakshina* (fees) to his guru, and hence cut off his thumb and gave it away, is considered worthy of respect, or Shravan, for whom the duty to serve his parents was the foremost in his life, is revered, or even Harishchandra, who gave up his kingdom, his wealth, his wife and children, to fulfil his duty to his people, is also awe-inspiring.

According to the *Bhagvada Gita*, any work that is rendered by 'duty' is considered sacred and most important. The 'law of duty' or 'dharma' in the *Bhagvada Gita* claims that true duty is one which is performed for the sake of the required action alone, and not for the reward at all. Sharvan did not anticipate any reward in return of his service. He did so, only because it was his duty as a son to serve his parents and look after their well-being.

Every person has certain duties to perform because of the position or place he is in. If he is a father, he must take care of his family; if he is a son, he must take care of his parents; if he is a master, he must take care of his servants; if he is a servant, he must serve his master as best as he can.

Titles in this Series

A Story of Devotion - Hanuman

A Story of Courage - Bhima

A Story of Duty - Shravan

A Story of Faithfulness - Sita